OVE

OVER THE MOON!

CHAMPIONSHIP FOOTBALL POEMS

With Contributions from Footballers and Poets

In association with the British Sports Association for the Disabled

RED FOX

A Red Fox Book

Published by Random House Children's Books
20 Vauxhall Bridge Road, London SW1V 2SA

A division of Random House UK Ltd
London Melbourne Sydney Auckland
Johannesburg and agencies throughout the world

1 3 5 7 9 10 8 6 4 2

First published simultaneously in hardback and paperback
by Hutchinson Children's Books and Red Fox 1996

Printed and bound in Great Britain by
Cox & Wyman, Reading, Berkshire

Papers used by Random House UK Ltd are natural, recyclable products made from wood grown in sustainable forests. The manufacturing processes conform to the environmental regulations of the country of origin.

RANDOM HOUSE UK Limited Reg. No. 954009

ISBN 0 09 968051 3

Cover photograph by kind permission of Professional Sport

With thanks to Kevin Hawkins

Just Me by Paul Gascoigne originally appeared in I Remember, I Remember, published by Red Fox, in 1993

CONTENTS

Foreword

LINFORD CHRISTIE

What a wonderful opportunity, to be offered the chance of writing a foreword for such a great compilation of poems.

Perhaps I should start by saying something about the charity that will receive the royalties from this book. It is fitting that it should be a sports organisation seeing as there are so many sporting personalities represented within these pages.

The British Sports Association for the Disabled, a registered charity, aims to provide, develop and co-ordinate a wide variety of sports and recreational opportunities for people with disabilities of all ages, ranging from the beginner to the elite disabled sportsman and sportswoman. The Association's work includes providing various innovative training opportunities, events, challenges and awards initiatives, as well as campaigning for increased disability awareness. BSAD also provides an information and advice support service. To achieve its objectives, the organisation works in partnership with other relevant agencies, including the British Paralympic Association (BPA) and the Sports Council.

Founded in 1961, BSAD is a national organisation with ten regional branches incorporating around 550 clubs, schools and affiliated associations. It has contact with sports for the disabled organisations around the world, including developing nations. The Association's funding includes grants from governing bodies, charitable trusts, commercial sponsorship and private donations, with an annual budget of £1.03 million. Volunteers are the lifeblood of BSAD and the Association recognises their valuable and fundamental role. They facilitate the Regional Executives in all regions, along with the local club structure and regional events. They organise the local groups, provide the management and trustees, give administrative support and undertake fund-raising and research.

On behalf of the Association, we hope you enjoy the poems and thank you for contributing to the future of disabled athletes.

SONG FOR EUROPE ... '96

To be sung to the tune of 'Jerusalem'

And did those feet, in flaming June,
Walk out on Wembley's hallowed green?
Britannia plays a welcoming tune
To host encounters European.
And did they qualify, the cream
Of Scotland, Spain and Germany?
Did Jackie Charlton's boys make the team
To meet England or Italy?

Bring out the men, worth more than gold
(Mercs now their chariots of fire)
As Gazza's fit, and Seaman bold,
May Platt and Shearer goals acquire.
Will Terry pick the team that's right?
His players cheered from every stand,
Till Europe hails its champions,
Let's pray they come from this fair land.

JIMMY HILL
CHAIRMAN, FULHAM FOOTBALL CLUB

THIRTEEN NIL

Oh the joy it was unbounded, what a thrill!
Selected for the team! I see him still,
At ten years old, what style and grace,
Those knobbly knees, that beaming face,
I felt as if *I'd* won the place ...
Thirteen nil.

The other team they swaggered round the field,
Our weaknesses, you might say, were revealed,
Oh my teeth I had to grit them,
If dogs had only bit them
Our side never knew what hit them ...
Thirteen nil.

The teacher bellowed insults and abuse
But even his support was not much use
It was a fate so mean and cruel,
No-one now was looking cool,
The laughing stock of all the school ...
Thirteen nil.

The brand new shin protectors brought no luck
The boy done bad: the striker never struck,
The ignominy and the shame,
To have missed the chance of fame,
And there was no-one else to blame,
Thirteen nil.

It was difficult to know just what to say,
As they all trooped off the pitch at close of play,
You couldn't say, 'Whew, that was close!
You were pipped right at the post!
Why don't we all propose a toast?'
To thirteen nil.

The score to shameful jeering was announced
Our lads annihilated: rudely trounced,
But there's one thing that's for sure,
Although the crowds they didn't roar,
Your mother loves you even more
At thirteen nil.

PAM AYRES

THE ANDERSON TWINS

What I remember
is this:

Miss Campbell, in her tartan mini-skirt
and high-heeled boots,

crossing the courtyard at dusk
in a current of snow,

and those two, playing football on the piece
of waste ground beside the canal,

stopping to watch, as she passed,
then resuming the game,

their bright blue jerseys
swimming away in the dark

and vanishing:
as if a ball, kicked far enough, could lead

from winter
to invisibility.

JOHN BURNSIDE

TWO LIMERICKS

There was a young player named Sleeper
Whose dream was to be a goalkeeper.
He jumped up so high
That his head hit the sky
And next he met the Grim Reaper!

There was a young striker called Mark
Who could not see in the dark
When a night match occurred
He mis-kicked a blackbird
And its friends chased him out of the park.

JOHN MOTSON
FOOTBALL COMMENTATOR

TONIGHT AT NOON
(with apologies to Adrian Henri)

Tonight at noon
John Motson will say,
'Oh to hell with statistics, let's just watch the game.'
A top manager will give a bung
To the Nicaragua solidarity campaign.
David Mellor will say, 'Yes,
I'm a prat; I don't deny that.'

Tonight at noon
The Queen will admit she hates
Having to watch the FA Cup Final.
Racist chanters will be laughed out the ground
And Tony Adams will take up contemporary dance.

Tonight at noon
The England team will have
Too many creative defenders.
Wimbledon F. C. will sign Roberto Baggio.

And tonight at noon
You will tell me
That you love me.

ARTHUR SMITH
AUTHOR OF *An Evening With Gary Lineker*

DON'T GIVE UP ON YOUR DREAMS

Cold winter nights training at Crewe,
Even when I had the flu,
To be a pro, this I had to do,
It would be hard work I knew,
But I wanted to be one of the few,
Who make it to the top,
And play in front of the 'Spion Kop'.

So the moral of this tale,
Never think you will fail,
Your dream can come true,
Whatever it is you want to do.

So when the going gets tough,
Never give up,
'Cause a 'Graham Souness' could turn up for you,
Just out of the blue,
And make your dreams come true.

ROB JONES
LIVERPOOL

PRE-SEASON TRAINING

Only one week to go now,
I must go for a run.
Or shall I go in the garden
And lie in the sun?

The first day back
Is like the first day of school.
Everyone's nervous
But tries to be cool.

They take our weights
And tell us we're fat.
But in four weeks' time
You'll see more fat on a gnat.

We're into the running
And boy is this tough.
Finally the boss shouts,
'Enough is enough.'

I'm crouched on all fours
And I'm starting to reach.
God, this time last week
I was lying on the beach.

Bodies are sprawled
And people throwing up.
But why do we do it?
To *win* the League (or a Cup).

DAVID HOWELLS
TOTTENHAM HOTSPUR

NORTH-EASTERN FANTASY HAIKU

Sunderland seven
Newcastle United nil
What a Saturday!

GRAEME CURRY

OH, PLEASE ...

Oh, please –
let me be in your team,
let mine be the name that you pick,
don't leave me to mope at the edge of the field,
resenting each jump and each kick;

I promise, I'll run like the wind,
I'll twist and I'll turn and I'll pass,
I'll dazzle defenders with sparkle
  and speed,
you won't see my boots touch the grass;

Or maybe, I'll play at the back,
as solid and strong as a wall,
frustrating all forwards who dare to attempt
the slightest approach with the ball;

But –
each time they play, it's the same,
I'm left on the line, in the cold,
they never allow me to join in the game,
they always say,
'Gran, you're too old!'

ROWENA SOMMERVILLE

FIRST MATCH

Fifteen years old,
Smart as paint,
Bright as ten buttons –
And off to The Match
With me Dad.

What? Me? Football? Never!

But ...
'You'd enjoy it,' says Dad.
'I'd like you to come.
Go on, pet. Just for me.'

So, here we are,
Dad and me,
Half-way up the Stand.
An hour gone by ...
And it's boring. Boring?
I'd sooner watch
Grass grow.

But suddenly ...
The crowd goes tense.
And it's Shackleton,
And the ball is at his feet,
And he's running,
And he's weaving,
And he's kicking it,
And it's sailing through the air,
And – it's a goal!

'Ha'way the lads!'
There's somebody shouting,
There's somebody screaming,
And leaping up and down,
And grinning like an idiot.
And what do you know?
That somebody's me.

My Dad grins.
'That's my lass!'
He tells the world.
'Why, man,
That's my bonny lass!'

JENNIFER CURRY

TWO LIMERICKS

There was a young man called Melly
Who thought he could play just like Pelé
So he went to Brazil
But was taken so ill
He could only watch Pelé on telly.

There was a young man called Paul
Who dreamed of playing football
He left his job up in Stafford
And went to Old Trafford
But now sells hot dogs at a stall.

GORDON BANKS
FORMER ENGLAND GOALKEEPER

INTERNATIONALS

Lined up in the backyard
We both call Wembley,
Me and my big brother, who's twenty-two,
  pick countries.
This is how the conversation goes:

What team you going to be then?
Can I be anybody?
It's your birthday, you be anybody you like.
I'll be England.
I raise my fist and shout,
ENGLAND – ENGLAND – ENGLAND –
  ENGLAND!
Except England, he says.
You said I could be anybody.
Except England. I'm always England.
Why are you always England?
It's a 'rule'.
Oh!

Who shall I be then?
You can be anybody you like.
Anybody? I'll be Brasil. Yeah!
I dance round doing the samba,
BRASIL – BRASIL – BRASIL – BRASIL!
Except Brasil.
Why can't I be Brasil?
Because I'm Brasil.
Who says?

The 'rule' says. I'm always Brasil except ...
Except?
Except when I'm England. That's the 'rule'.
Oh!
Who shall I be then?
It's your birthday. Be who you want.
Anybody at all?
Anybody in the whole world.
I'll be Man U.
I jump in the air shouting,
MAN U – MAN U – MAN U – MAN U!
Except Man U.
Why can't I be Man U?
Because it's a club. Clubs don't play
  countries.
Who says I have to be a country?
The 'rule' says.
Oh!

Think of somebody else.
Anybody?
Anybody in the whole world.
But I can't think of any other countries.
You could be your school team.
Schools can't play countries.
Yes, they can. It's a 'rule'.
Oh!

I'll be Weld Park Primary Under 9's. Yeah!
WELD PARK PRIMARY UNDER 9's –
  WELD PARK PRIMARY UNDER 9's –
  WELD PARK PRIMARY UNDER 9's –
  WELD PARK PRIMARY UNDER 9's!

So it's Weld Park Primary Under 9's v.
  Brasil at Wembley.
And Weld Park score in the first minute. Yes!
Offside by miles.
Oh, come on!
Are you arguing with the ref?
Ref? You can't be Brasil and the ref.
Yes, I can. It's a 'rule'.
No it's not.
Yellow card for arguing with the ref.
Oh ref! Diabolical decision.
And it's the red card for Weld Park Primary
  Under 9's.
Ah ref, you can't send off a whole team.
Yes, I can. It's a 'rule'.
Oh!

Sitting in disgrace upon the bench
I ask him when do I get to make the rules.
When you're grown up and mature like me,
  he explains,
Sliding home Brasil's winner
And dancing his victory jig around the flower
  beds,
While I make for my birthday cake
And an early bath.

GARETH OWEN

JASON'S TRIAL

Jason was a football freak;
He really loved the game:
To be a first-class footballer
Was his one aim.

He practised every day and played
Again each night in dream;
When he was twelve they chose him for
The school's first team.

He was quite brilliant. Five years passed
And – though rarely this occurs –
It seemed his dreams might all come true:
He was given a trial by Spurs.

He played a blinder on the day;
The spectators cheered and roared,
And after the match he was asked to appear
Before the Selection Board.

The Chairman said, 'I've got the reports
From our experts who watched you play:
Your speed and ball-control were fine;
For tackling you get an A.

'And when our striker scored his goal
You were first to jump on his back,
And when *you* scored you punched the air
Before you resumed the attack.

‘So far, so good; but you were weak
On the thing our lads do best;
It seems you hardly spat at all,
So you failed the spitting-test.

‘But don’t despair. If you go home
And practise every day
You still might learn to spit with style
In the true professional way.’

VERNON SCANNELL

JUST ME

I'm a professional footballer
lying in a hospital bed
thinking of all those nasty things
all going through my head.

I know I should not be lying here
it's because of Wembley
thinking of that stupid tackle
instead of all that glee.

Now when I do get out of here
I'll be working on this knee
getting fit left, right and centre
just thinking of Italy.

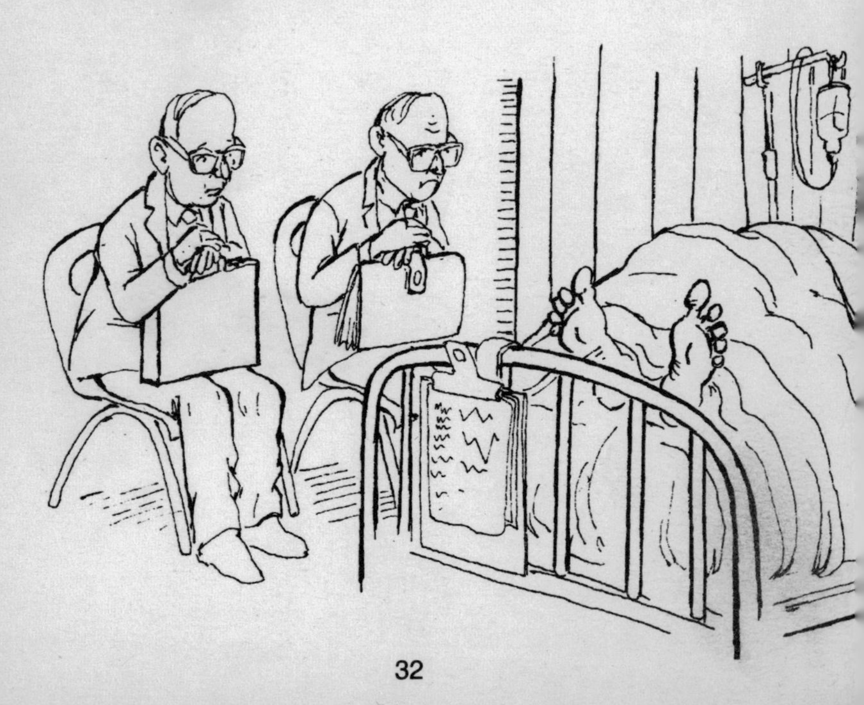

Now what is in my mind right now
no-one will ever know
but when I'm given that big, big chance
it will be a one-man show.

Now Mel and Len both work for me
both working day and night
one's an accountant, one's a lawyer
making sure I'm alright.

Now please don't worry about a thing
I know I'm getting thinner
but at the back of my mind
there'll only be one winner.

PAUL GASCOIGNE
RANGERS

STRIP

He's got it.
It cost a lot
weeks of waiting and saving up,
Mum paying half and the rest
part of his Christmas present.

He's put it on
in the bedroom
for the very first time,
he's gone downstairs looking like everything
he ever wanted. Shining.

He's playing
better than ever,
he'll get picked for the team
if he keeps this up. Weeks
of wearing the strip,
Mum grabbing it off him to wash it.

One day out shopping
in town with Mum
he's into extra time
with the crowd roaring him on.
Two big boys shove ahead of him.

They're laughing.
Look at that idiot.
Doesn't he know they've got a new strip?

HELEN DUNMORE

AND HERE ARE THE FOOTBALL RESULTS

BLACKBURN 3 .... HALF PAST 4
CHELSEA 4 .... AFTER 8
WEST HAM 2 .... JAWS 3
LEEDS 1 ....FAMOUS 5
NEWCASTLE 0 .... SECRET 7
EVERTON 2 ....M1
QPR 1 .... QE 2
BOLTON 3 ....PAGE 3
LIVERPOOL 6 ....SEVEN 11
MAN UNITED 1 .... FIGURE 8

PETER DIXON

THE GAME, OR IS IT?

The game has gone from strength to strength
Even now reaching unknown depth and length.
Or is it just a game we play,
Only to while the time away?
Both men and boys expressing joy,
Showing off to the girls on the side
Puffing up with pride
As they score a goal.

Despite the constant falling rain
And howling in pain from a foul again.
Yet bravely we play on. I mean what can you do?
The girls on the side are watching you.

I love the game
But it's just not the same.
Certain ones come to the grounds
Causing trouble, milling around,
Ugly racist comments,
Designed to disillusion and discourage.
How these things can weigh you down.

But is this game just a game,
Or does it have a greater claim?
Football has a language all its own
That has to be used and made known.
Football has surpassed creed and colour
And has so much more to offer.

For football, international barriers have
  come down.
People have come from all around.
Let's use it to bring the people together
Maybe to make a better future.

JOHN FASHANU
FORMER ASTON VILLA

A LIMERICK

'Tell my mum I'm OK if she phones,'
Said the fullback with two broken bones.
'Just hear what I say
The next time you play,
Don't try to *nutmeg* Vinny Jones!'

GRAEME TOMLINSON
MANCHESTER UNITED

OH, HOW I LOVE MY FOOTBALL BOOTS

Oh, how I love my football boots,
With all their cuts and tears;
I wish I was a centipede,
And owned a hundred pairs!

(A hundred boots to play in,
And the other hundred, spares.)

MICHAEL RATNETT

MY FIRST GAME

I dreamt last night that my boots had turned into
  jelly sweets
With liquorice strings for laces
Studs made out of dolly mixtures.
The dream was so real I jumped out of bed
Fumbling across the dark floor, stubbing my toe,
I shouted out, 'My boots.'
There they lay at the foot of my bed
Cleaned, polished – normal.

Lights flooded on and in came Dad.
'Are you all right – not worrying about tomorrow
  in the school team?'
'No, I'm OK,' I lied.
I went back to sleep;
I dreamt my goal net was full of swimming goldfish.

JOHN MOTSON'S SON, FREDERICK
AGED 9

FAIR GAME!

Clear off! You're not playing!
This game's not for you!
Why've you stuck your nose in here?
No-one asked you to.

Your legs are thin as tent-pegs,
Couldn't kick a cat!
Can't you see your face don't fit?
Sorry, but that's that!

Cool it! Keep your hair on!
You're too late, anyway –
Samantha picked her team last night,
I picked mine today.

Y'what! You're playing for Sammy!
She wants you on the wing!
But she's the one who said: 'NO BOYS!
BOYS WRECK EVERYTHING!'

So! Sammy's switched the rules, then!
Two can play at that –
Look, *please*, *please* join our side instead,
They're a bunch of *tat*!

I swear I would've picked you,
But Sammy's such a cheat ...
Hey, Sammy! Eat your heart right out!
***We've* got Pete 'The Feet'!**

GINA WILSON

SPOT THE BALL

Jimmy Tully was a sad and sorry kid:
The big match was coming up
But he was in bed with chicken pox
In his granny's cramped and dingy flat.

If only his mum had been at home
She'd know that nothing must stop
Him trotting down to the football ground
And Town's chance of winning the Cup.

A tear dribbled down onto Ryan Giggs
Framed in a picture from *Shoot*.
Why did mum have to win the lottery
And take off with that geezer from *Loot*?

Now Gran had even got rid of his ticket
And got a good price for it too.
So she'd popped off to the bookie's shop
Counting the tenners in two's.

If only he were Tommy, the White Ranger
He'd morph into a pigeon and fly ...
Suddenly he saw a shadow at the window
But t'were only his Aunty Vi.

'I've come as your footie angel,
Hop on me bike and hold tight.
I'm dropping you at St Dude's Park
Old Granny's not gonna win this fight.'

Nicholas Allan '96

Jimmy's heart was a football at Eric Cantona's feet.
Flicked, tricked, bounced and juggled as Vi's moped
hit the street.
But his footie shirt mocked his chicken pox
When the ticket office read 'Sold Out'.

'I'm sorry, love,' spluttered Aunty Vi.
Jimmy threw his shirt to the ground,
Just as Lee Lark, Town's handsome captain
Ran up, startling everybody around.

'Hey laddie, you're just what we need,
Our sponsors have let us down.
All the lads have got new kit
But mascot's strip's been sent t'wrong town.'

Suddenly there was footie daylight.
Town's new strip was all red spots,
Which is why Jimmy Tully, the mascot,
Led out his team in only shorts and socks
– And they won 3 – 2.

NEIL WEBB
NOTTINGHAM FOREST

MATCH POSTPONED

The only geography
I ever learned
was radio:

the gold names
shining through
a matt-black glass:

Madrid; Belgrade;
the farmlights of Oslo
and Sottens;

and final scores: imagining a field
of snow and lights, and people walking home
in duffel coats and tightly knotted scarves,

from Heart of Midlothian,
Alloa,
Queen of the South.

JOHN BURNSIDE

FOOTBALL!

  Football! *Football!*
The boys want the entire playground
and we're left squashed
against the broken fence.
Why don't the teachers stop them?
  Why?
Haven't they got *any* sense?

My friend Anna
ran across the tarmac. Smack!
Got the football right on her nose.
Blood all over her face.
Why don't the teachers do something?
Why?
It's a disgrace, *a disgrace!*

Those boys ... I mean
they're like hooligans.
CHEL-SEA! CHEL-SEA! they chant
morning, noon and night.
The teacher on duty does ... nothing.
Why?
It's just, it's just not right.

We complain bitterly
but the duty teacher says,
'Go see the Head. He's in charge.'
Him! He's *useless*. YOU-ESS-LESS!
When we ask him to ban football
Why,
oh why, can't he just say 'Yes'?

WES MAGEE

A WAY OF LIFE

Football is a way of life,
It helps to pay the bills –
New dresses for the wife
And paint for the windowsills!

Two hours of training every day,
With one day off a week.
One game at home, then one away –
We hope, without defeat!

An easy living, some may think
To live and make ends meet.
To celebrate, we'll have a drink.
Now that's an easy feat!

AIDEN DAVISON
BOLTON WANDERERS

EPITAPH FOR NUMBER NINE

Our centre forward's passing
Has been United's loss.
His final words were 'On me head'
So there we placed this cross.

IAN WHYBROW

IT'S ALL ICED CHAMPAGNE IN THE KING'S ROAD

It's different below in the dressing room before
a match.
There's no iced Bolly, no King's road dollies,
None of the mass hysteria of up top in the stands.
Just an implicit notion that something is bound
to happen.

There will be a reckoning – not today perhaps,
Not tomorrow either – but you WILL pay.
Yes, this is how it is with just seconds to go;
Your skull is aching like it's ready to burst.

Finally the door opens – the tunnel awaits,
Your studs clatter and clatter on the concrete.
You look at your opponents just two yards away,
All massive hairy legs and rock-hard columns of
muscle.

Then you think of the irony of it all,
Maybe 40,000 fans up top all envying you.
And you? Right now, you would love to be up top
With the iced champagne and the King's Road
dollies.

Yet you know that when concrete yields to turf,
When your irritating studs cease their incessant
chatter,
And you start weaving your magic in and around
the box,
It will all be OK as the game takes over.

PETER OSGOOD
FORMER CHELSEA, SOUTHAMPTON AND ENGLAND
with
GREG TESSER
HIS AGENT

DICK THE DIVER

Dick was lousy at dribbling
He wasn't much good on the ball
What he brought to the game
Was always the same –
A hundred and one ways how to fall.

He fell when somebody tackled him
Just in front of the referee
He'd crash to the ground
Then roll around
As the crowd all screamed 'PENALTEE!'

The ref would have no doubt about it
Wouldn't even pause to think
Ball on the spot
Powerful shot
'Cheers, ref,' Dick would say with a wink.

But one day Dick got his comeuppance
He'd been diving all over the place
Again and again
He'd be screaming in pain
Then jump up, with a smile on his face.

One-nil, two-nil, three-nil
Each goal was scored thanks to Dick
Sometimes when he fell
The crowd would yell
'Ere, ref, where's your white stick?'

But then a woman left the ranks of spectators
'Oh no,' muttered Dick, 'it's my mum'
He trembled with fear
As she grabbed his ear
Then kicked him hard up the bum.

'You're a total disgrace!' said Dick's mother
As, behind the ref, Dick tried to cower
'You've got two left feet
You're a bloomin' cheat
Wanna dive? Go dive in the shower.'

Sent off by his very own mother
Dick the diver's shame was complete
Today you can trap him
Or trip him or hack him
But he'll *always* stay on his feet.

TERENCE BLACKER

MS JONES, FOOTBALL TEACHER

Ms Jones,
  football teacher,
red shellsuit,
  flash boots.
She laughs
  as she centres,
shrieks 'GOAL!'
  when she
    shoots!

Ms Jones,
  what a creature,
pink lipstick,
  shin pads.
See there
  on the touchline
lots of
  bug-eyed
    lads.

Ms Jones'
  finest feature,
long blond hair
  – it's neat.
She back heels
  and bend kicks;
she's fast
  on her
    feet.

Ms Jones,
  football teacher,
told us,
  'Don't give up!'
She made us
  train harder
and we
  won the
    Cup!

WES MAGEE

THE GHOSTS OF PARK AVENUE

Between the terraces the grasses blow
and nod the setting sun from head to head.
This is a place with nowhere else to go.
As people switch the TV on and settle down
and shadows lengthen from the houses round about,
you listen and you almost hear a shout, a thud,
the hush as the cross hangs, and the long
outrush of a moan as the shot dies, wide again.

Against the barriers the sycamores and elders
sway, shoulder to shoulder. The play
of the wind swings. They are rooted to their spot:
they know they must stay to the bitter end.
This is a place where time has begun
to turn in on itself, to find only the memory
of Saturdays, of afternoons where no-one scored
and the bored crowd heckled and sang
for the sake of it, and shuffled home to a kettle
and the classifieds, and game-shows where
at least somebody just like them could win.

Now, when the stanchions and the roofs have gone,
only the steps and low brick walls remain.
The nights come washing over them, and the moon,
white as a floodlight, rises and spreads
its monochrome — and from the tunnel
in twin rows, the teams, running, their shorts
flapping like washday, silently.
And the terrace, silently, responds: the roar
of fifteen thousand hopeful souls.
These are not men but legends that will fade
as dreams do at morning. Till then,
they weave the tall grass with their artistry,
and someone, somewhere in his deepest sleep,
picks up a pass, and sensing glory, twists
and jinks past the back and heads for goal.

STUART HENSON

OVER THE MOON

All over the moon they play football,
All over the moon up in space,
All over the moon every crater and dune,
Boasts a team of an alien race.

Their shirts are the colours of rainbows,
Their skins are a stardusty grey,
And the boots on their toes all have suckers in rows,
There to keep them from floating away.

They play with a meteorite football;
To head it they wear a steel hat,
And the ref's a surprise with his seven green eyes,
But they still say he's blind as a bat.

I watched the Cup Final on Saturnday,
The Allstars played Moonchester Town;
And everyone went, every moongirl and gent,
For the tickets were just half a crown.

And the match that they saw was a wonder,
For both sides had chances galore,
The ball dipped and curled, it was out of this world,
And yet no-one seemed able to score.

The ninetieth minute was ending,
It looked like the match was all done –
Then the 'Stars' Number Five smashed a rocketing
drive,
A GOAL! And the final was won!

Number Five took the cup from the Moonking,
As the crowd cheered for all they were worth,
And they asked was he pleased with the trophy he squeezed,
And he said, 'Well, I'm over the Earth!'

MICHAEL RATNETT

TRANSMUTATION OF A CROWD

Half-time, it was magic,
it was over the constellations,
for at the floodlit match,
one man with a flute
jumped the barrier.
Soon three policemen,
all threat, tried to catch him.
The crowd began to shout,
'Gerroff. Leave him alone.'
Then the lights went out.
Sudden, also, the silence.

When the flautist played
such a small pure melody,
thousands in the dark stadium
assumed a weird dignity.
Behind steering clouds,
surely the proud stars listened
and would have cheered?
Then the mystic music ceased,
the floodlighting resumed,
and, soluble, into the crowd
the flautist disappeared.

Near the dying of the game
home-team losing, 1 – 3,
boiling fans jeered their own
tame centre-forward and
the cataract-afflicted referee.

Heaving the same khaki oaths,
they became shameless as war.
As for me, I would tell you more,
much more about that flute-player,
his proverbs and his parables,
if I but knew his name.

DANNIE ABSE